COLOUR SONGS AND RHYMES

Illustrated by Geoffrey Butcher.

In this book and accompanying cassette all the colours of the rainbow are presented to children for their information and enjoyment. Young children can learn about colours in many ways; when they are dressing and undressing, when they are working with their toys, when they are out and about using their eyes and asking questions. To sing songs and chant rhymes about colours helps to increase their awareness of colour and reinforce the knowledge they are gaining. This is not only pleasurable, but is a basic skill which will be very valuable later at school when learning to describe things and identify similarities and differences.

At the back of the book you will find additional notes for parents or teachers about the rhymes.

COLOUR SONGS AND RHYMES

PAGE

1 Roses are red
2 I've got a fine new kite
4 Hector Protector
6 White sand and grey sand
7 Jolly red nose
8 Rainbow
10 It's snowing, it's blowing
12 Watch my hens
13 Brown potatoes
14 Green, green, green
16 Tick tack too
18 Farmer Howe
20 Lavender's blue
22 Ripe cherries
24 Bubbles from my pipe

First published 1974 by
Three Four Five Publishing Ltd
This edition published 1985 by
Macdonald & Co (Publishers) Ltd
London & Sydney

A BPCC plc company

Macdonald & Co (Publishers) Ltd Maxwell House 74 Worship Street
London EC2A 2EN

ISBN 0 356 11259 4

Roses are red

Roses are red, violets are blue,
Sugar is sweet, and so are you.

I've got a fine new kite

I've got a fine new kite, scarlet bright,
Tail a-trailing, blow wind and toss it, please,
Over the trees, far a-sailing.

I've got a fine new kite, lemon bright,
Tail a-trailing, blow wind and toss it, please,
Over the trees, far a-sailing.

I've got a fine new kite, purple bright,
Tail a-trailing, blow wind and toss it, please,
Over the trees, far a-sailing.

I've got a fine new kite, emerald bright,
Tail a-trailing, blow wind and toss it, please,
Over the trees, far a-sailing.

Hector Protector

Hector Protector was dressed all in green,
Hector Protector was sent to the queen.
The queen did not like him, no more did the king,
So Hector Protector was sent back again.

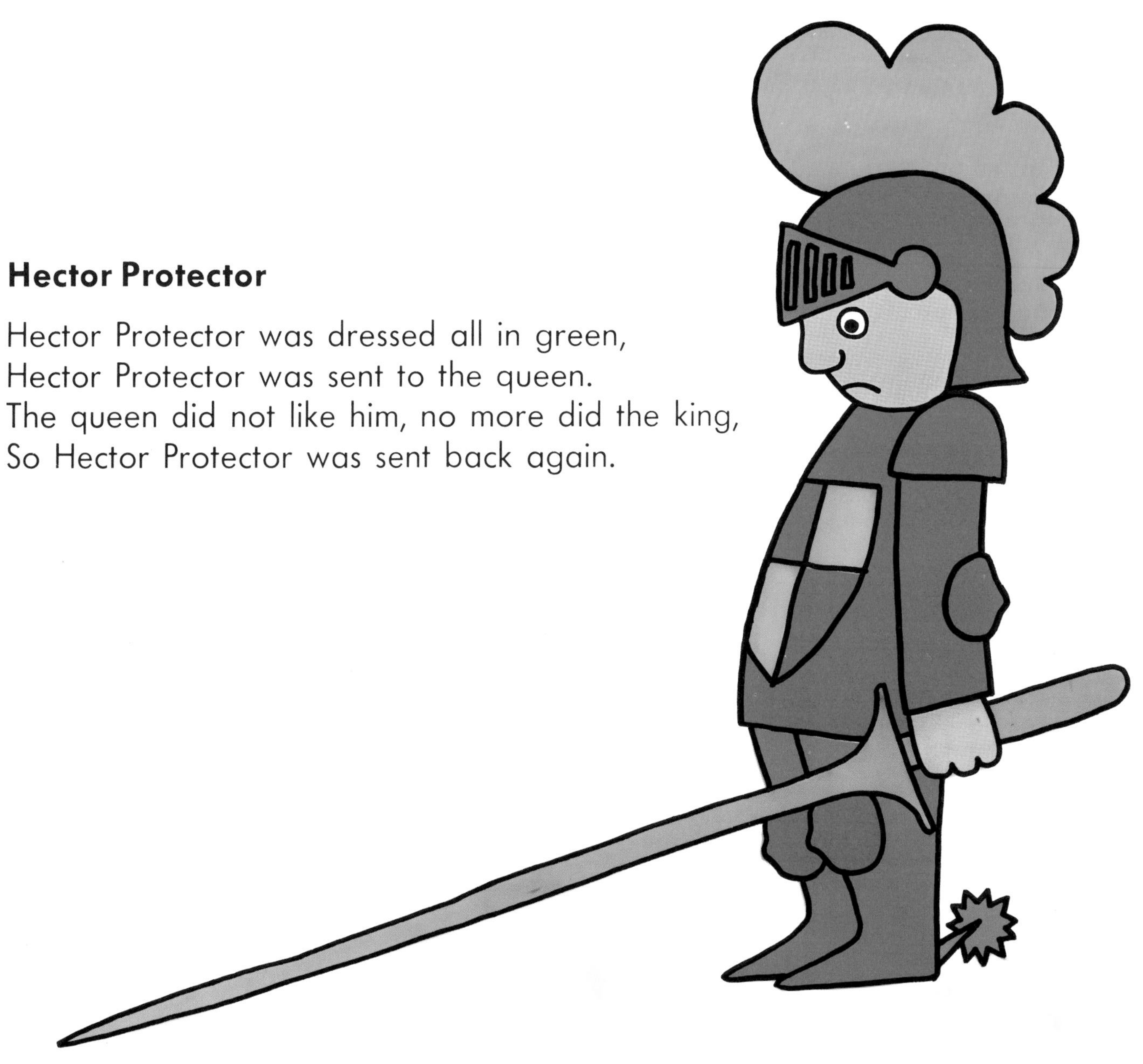

White sand and grey sand

White sand and grey sand.
Who'll buy my grey sand?
Who'll buy my white sand?

Brown sand and yellow sand.
Who'll buy my yellow sand?
Who'll buy my brown sand?

Red sand and orange sand.
Who'll buy my orange sand?
Who'll buy my red sand?

Jolly red nose

Nose, nose, jolly red nose,
And what gave thee that jolly red nose?
Nutmeg and ginger, cinnamon and cloves,
That's what gave me this jolly red nose.

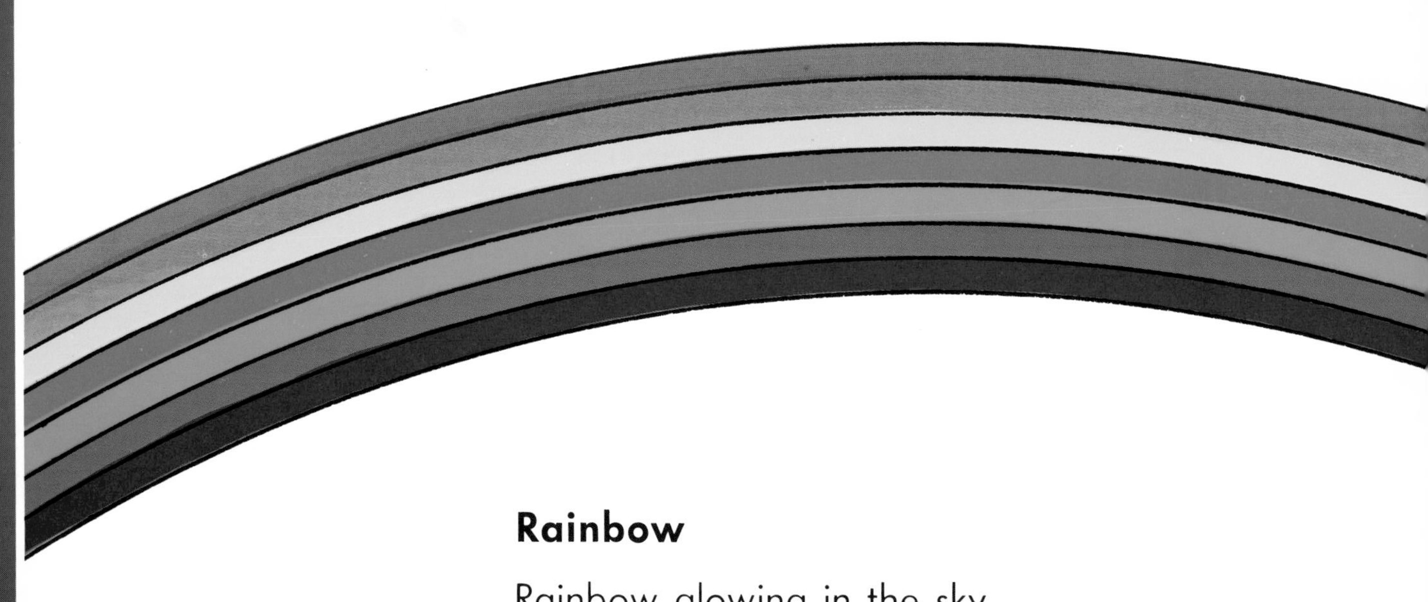

Rainbow

Rainbow glowing in the sky,
Rainbow flowers are growing by.
Violet, indigo, red and blue,
Colours of the rainbow's hue.
Yellow, orange, soft fresh green,
All the colours to be seen.
Rainbow glowing in the sky,
Rainbow flowers are growing by.

It's snowing, it's blowing

It's snowing, it's blowing,
But I am safe from harm,
For I shall wear a yellow pair
Of gloves to keep me warm.

It's snowing, it's blowing,
But I am safe from harm,
For I shall wear a lilac pair
Of pants to keep me warm.

It's snowing, it's blowing,
But I am safe from harm,
For I shall wear an orange pair
Of socks to keep me warm.

It's snowing, it's blowing,
But I am safe from harm,
For I shall wear a purple pair
Of boots to keep me warm.

Watch my hens

Watch my hens and you will see,
They walk always one, two, three.
First the black one leads the line,
Then the white with feathers fine.
Brownie follows last, and she
Makes the third one, you will see.

Brown potatoes

Brown potatoes, white potatoes,
Change them if you can.
Turn them into golden chips,
Frying in the pan.

Green, green, green

Green, green, green, is everything I'm wearing,
Green, green, green, my only clothes shall be.
Why do I always dress myself in green?
Because a forester is the one I love.

Blue, blue, blue, is everything I'm wearing,
Blue, blue, blue, my only clothes shall be.
Why do I always dress myself in blue?
Because a sailor is the one I love.

Red, red, red, is everything I'm wearing,
Red, red, red, my only clothes shall be.
Why do I always dress myself in red?
Because a fireman is the one I love.

Black, black, black, is everything I'm wearing,
Black, black, black, my only clothes shall be.
Why do I always dress myself in black?
Because a miner is the one I love.

White, white, white, is everything I'm wearing,
White, white, white, my only clothes shall be.
Why do I always dress myself in white?
Because a baker is the one I love.

Bright, bright, bright, is everything I'm wearing,
Bright, bright, bright, my only clothes shall be.
Why do I always dress in bright colours?
Because an artist is the one I love.

Tick tack too

Tick tack too,
Mend a lady's shoe.
A red shoe, a red shoe,
Tick tack too.

Tick tack too,
Mend a man's shoe.
A black shoe, a black shoe,
Tick tack too.

Tick tack too,
Mend a baby's shoe.
A pink shoe, a pink shoe,
Tick tack too.

Tick tack too,
Mend a boy's shoe.
A brown shoe, a brown shoe,
Tick tack too.

Tick tack too,
Mend a girl's shoe.
A blue shoe, a blue shoe,
Tick tack too.

Farmer Howe

Farmer Howe, farmer Howe,
Farmer Howe has one brown cow.

Farmer Penn, farmer Penn,
Farmer Penn has one white hen.

Farmer Mogg, farmer Mogg,
Farmer Mogg has one black hog.

Farmer Beddow, farmer Beddow,
Farmer Beddow has one green meadow.

Farmer Higgs, farmer Higgs,
Farmer Higgs has ten pink pigs.

Lavender's blue

Lavender's blue diddle, diddle,
Lavender's green,
When I am king, diddle, diddle,
You shall be queen.

Call up your men diddle, diddle,
Set them to work,
Some to the plough, diddle, diddle,
Some to the cart.

Some to make hay diddle, diddle,
Some to cut corn,
While you and I, diddle, diddle,
Keep ourselves warm.

Lavender's blue diddle, diddle,
Lavender's green,
When I am king, diddle, diddle,
You shall be queen.

Ripe cherries

Come, let's go and gather ripe cherries,
I know a place where many grow.
Red and black and white and golden,
One, two, three, on every row.
Val-e-ri,   Val-e-ra.
Val-e-ri,   Val-e-ra.
One, two and three on every row.

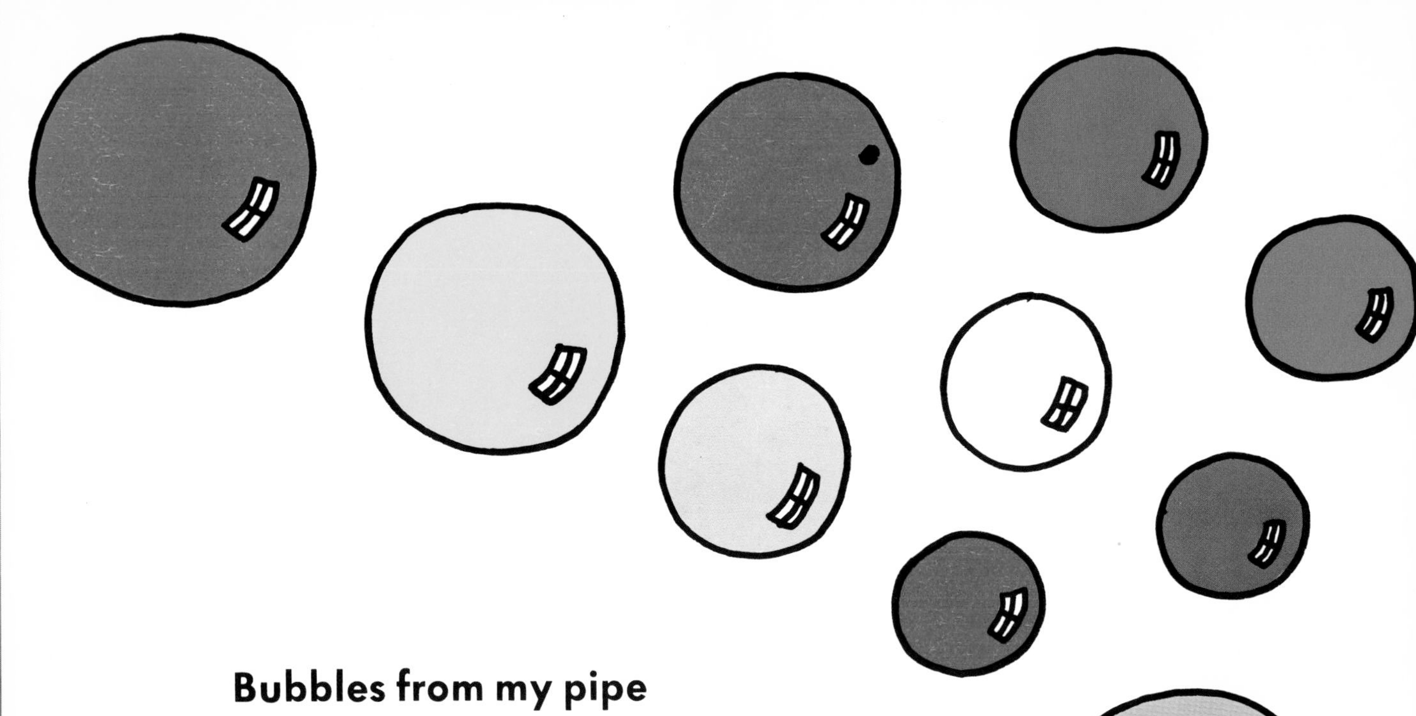

Bubbles from my pipe

Bubbles from my pipe I blow,
Red, yellow, in the air,
Orange, green, off they go,
Blue, white, everywhere.

Bubbles from my pipe I blow,
Pink, violet, in the air,
Red, purple, off they go,
Rainbows, everywhere.

Notes:

Colours are everywhere! These songs and rhymes give constant opportunity to point away from the book to colours in the house, in the garden, in clothes, toys, crayons, magazines and so on. All of this reinforces the knowledge gained, encourages an understanding of the benefit of learning, and adds excitement to the constant process of discovery.

Children who have learned the songs and rhymes in this book will start to notice colour, and will start to use words like *'tan', 'gold', 'silver'* and *'navy blue',* far beyond its scope. The thing to remember is that this is all building awareness, vocabulary, initiative and will develop a valuable sense of comparison and fitness, skills which will be of enormous value at school.

Colour blindness:

Many parents worry about colour blindness in their children, and their worry is usually groundless. Nevertheless very occasionally colour blindness does exist, probably over only a small range of the spectrum.

It is far better to know about it and be able to allow for it than to ignore it.